Treasures by the Sea Workbook
For ages 8-12

27 Bible Truths for Kids
An Adventure in Discovering God
Through His Word and Creation

Sally Streib
David Valentin

SEA WAY Books™
Sea n' See Presentations

www.seansee.net

Note to parents, teachers, and readers.

This workbook is designed for use with the story book, *Treasures by the Sea,* by Sally Streib. Each workbook lesson enhances the lessons learned by the main characters, Eric and Susan in *Treasures by the Sea.* Chapter numbers in the workbook correspond with the chapters of the same number in the story book.

For the best learning results, read the corresponding story of Eric and Susan, then complete the matching lesson in the workbook.

Teachers may also wish to purchase a copy of the *Teachers Edition,* available from the publisher.

The answers to the Bible study questions in this workbook will work with the *King James Version* and *The Clear Word, an Expanded Paraphrase of the Bible to Nurture Faith and Growth,* by Jack J. Blanco, published by Review and Herald Publishing Association.

Treasures by the Sea, by Sally Streib
27 Bible Truths for Kids
27 Bible Truths for Kids, Teachers Edition
are available from:

> Sea n' See Presentations
> > 1783 Forest Drive #221
> > Annapolis, Maryland 21401-4229

> Online at:
> > www.seansee.net

> Your local Adventist Book Center
> > www.adventistbookcenter.comm

ISBN 0-9711104-0-9
$10.95 U.S./$15.50 Can.

© 2004 Sally Streib, David Valentin
ISBN-13 978-0-9711104-2-7
ISBN-10 0-9711104-2-5

Published by:
Sea n' See Presentations
Cover & Book Design, Illustrations by: David Valentin.
Cover Illustration by Clara Hicks

Table of Contents

Table of Illustrations

Storm Clouds

You Can Ask God "Why?"

Eric and Susan went to live in California with Aunt Sally after their mother died in a car accident. They felt scared. Susan found it easy to ask questions, but Eric was different. He wanted to understand why his mother had been killed by a drunk driver, but every time he started to talk about the accident, he froze up inside.

Like Susan and Eric, you may have questions. You may be asking, "Where can I find answers?" "Who will listen to me and help me?"

Your questions are important. God knows that having questions is part of growing up. He wants to help you figure things out. That's why He prepared answers to your questions years ago. He placed them in the Bible and the Book of Nature. He knew you would search for answers and He wanted to be sure you could find them. He also puts people in your life who can help you.

Open your Bible and find the answers to the questions below. They may be the very ones you've been asking.

And, don't be afraid to ask someone you trust. They'll be glad to talk with you and help you think things through.

Dive Into The Bible

1. How can I know that God cares when I hurt inside? The Bible says, "The Lord is
   _____ to the broken hearted." Psalms 34:18

2. Sometimes I have questions that I'm afraid to ask. God promises me that if I
   _____ and ask, I will receive what I need. Matthew 21:22

3. When something happens that makes me afraid, I can do what David did when he
   felt scared. Read Psalms 56:3. I can choose to _____ God.

4. God put answers to my questions in the Bible. What other place can I look for
   answers? _____ Romans 1:20

5. God promises to send the _____ _____ to comfort me
   and _____ me. John 14:26

Search For Buried Treasure

Questions are good, but answers can be hard to find. What are three ways to find answers to your questions?

1. _____

2. _____

3. _____

Write the name of one person you trust to talk to:

_____

If you could ask God anything, what would it be? Write your question below.

_____

_____

_____

_____

Jump Into the
Tide Pool Zone

Get set for adventure. In each of the following lessons you will explore the tide pool zone that runs along the rocky North American coastline. Winds, storms, and waves carve out places in the cliffs that hold water and provide homes for hundreds of creatures.

God painted these creatures with bold colors. He made them creep, crawl, slither, and swish. They are covered with hairs, slime, and scales.

Twice a day, tides that are controlled by the moon, send a surge of water into the pools and remove it as the sea pulls back toward the outer ocean.

Upwellings, or bursts of water from the sea bottom, mix with the surface water providing food and oxygen for the many creatures and plants that live in the pools.

Aunt Sally, the author of Treasures by the Sea, has explored California tide pools for years. She takes Eric and Susan on treasure hunts, climbing over rocks and peering into pools. Join them and discover for yourself the good news of a God who made the fantastic creatures and who created you.

Your Choice

I am learning that I can ask questions. I see that God has made ways for me to understand Him and my world. I want to know more about God and His Son, Jesus. I want to know how He put answers in nature.

Sign your name here: _____

CHAPTER 2

Aunt Sally's Cliffs

Creation

Eric and Susan awoke early on their first morning at Aunt Sally's beach home. They joined her as she walked down to the narrow stretch of sand just beyond the house. They climbed up and down cliffs that stuck ragged toes into the ocean. At the edge of a pool of water caught in the rocks, Aunt Sally stooped down and picked up a round shell. "This is an abalone," she said.

When the twins first looked at the abalone, they didn't feel very excited because it looked like a plain, round rock.

When Aunt Sally removed the creature from the shell they looked inside and discovered hundreds of rainbow colors that sparkled in the sunlight. Eric and Susan learned to look closer.

Getting to know God is a lot like learning about a new sea creature. The closer you look, the more you see, and the more excited you get.

Nature, a book without pages, teaches exciting truths about God. Studying nature will help you know what God is like. The closer you look, the more you learn. When you see how beautiful God is, you will say, "I want to be God's friend."

Dive Into The Bible

1. The Bible says, "In the beginning _____ created the

   _____ and the _____." Genesis 1:1

2. God used His hands to_____ the world. Isaiah 45:12

3. How do I know that I'm important to God? The Bible says that God made me

   _____. Genesis 1:27

4. God was happy with all the things He made. He said that everything was very

   _____. Genesis 1:31

5. God loves me. He calls His love for me _____. Jeremiah 31:3

6. God not only loves me, He wants to call me His _____. John 15:15

Search For Buried Treasure

Group Discussion

Do all people believe that God created them? What are some of their ideas? Read: Genesis Chapter I.

Nature Activity

Make a list of your five favorite creatures in your Nature Notebook.
Search for the nearest location where these creatures live. It may be your house, a zoo, or a farm.
Draw a picture of each creature, placing them in the habitat where they live.
Write down two reasons why you like each creature. What makes them special?

Create: bring into existence
Image: person or thing that resembles another
Friend: person with whom one enjoys mutual affection and regard
Word: command, order, decree, instruction

Words to Know

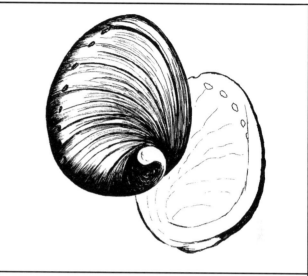

Black Abalone

Description: Plump, oval shell growing to be 6" long and 2-4" wide. Smooth, black outer shell. Pearly, multi-colored interior. Colors change with food supply.

Habitat: Clings to rocks from high tide line to 20' deep. Selects surf-swept cliffs from Alaska to California where brown algae grows.

Comments: Abundant on California coast. Preyed upon by crabs, octopus, and sea otters. Escapes by spitting out cloud of white mucous. Gallops away with large flexible foot. Eight holes in the shell take in food and pump out waste.

Your Choice

I have learned that God created the world. He created me in His own image. All around me, I can see things that God created. I believe that God loves me. He has called me His friend and child. I want to be His friend.

Sign your name here: _____

Celebration Day

The Sabbath Day

Eric and Susan were surprised when they discovered Aunt Sally in the kitchen making preparations for a special day she called Sabbath. She explained that God felt very happy about the world He created in six days. He decided to set the seventh day apart as a special time to celebrate His wonderful work.

Imagine that you have just finished an exciting school assignment. You look your project over and like what you see. All your hard work has paid off. Now it's time for a break. You call several friends and invite them over to your house so they can share your excitement. This is just what God did. When He finished creating the world, He announced a celebration day and called it the Sabbath.

Before Adam and Eve got busy exploring their garden home, God told them about His Sabbath. "I will meet you here," He may have said, "Let's spend the whole day together."

Are you surprised that God created a day like Sabbath just for you? How can you spend a whole day with God? What does this mean? Read the following verses. They will answer your questions.

Dive Into The Bible

1. What did God do when He finished creating the world? He _____. Genesis 2:2

2. How do I know God wants me to pay attention to the Sabbath? God says to _____ the Sabbath. Exodus 20:8

3. Which day did God set aside as special? The Bible says that the _____ day is the Sabbath day. Exodus 20:10

4. How long will the Sabbath be a special time to get together with God? It will _____. Isaiah 66:22 and 23

5. When does the Sabbath begin and end? It begins at _____ and ends at _____. Leviticus 23:32

Search For Buried Treasure

Group Discussion

Why is the Sabbath so exciting? How can I make it the best day of the week? What does it mean to keep the Sabbath day holy?
Read: Leviticus 23:3, Acts 13:44, John 9:14.

A day just for you!

The Sabbath has been a special day for a very long time. Can you find the first verse in the Bible that mentions the Sabbath? Write the verse below.

_____

Have you ever played Hide and Seek? If you think that God is hiding from you, then the Sabbath is just what you need. A whole day to look for God. If you take time to seek Him on His special day, you will _____ Him.
Jeremiah 29:12-13

Did Jesus celebrate God's special day? Read Luke 4:16 to find out.

Things you can do next Sabbath to build your love for Jesus.

> Take a walk in the woods.
> Snorkel over a coral reef and name the fish.
> Help someone who is stuck inside because of illness.
> Collect flowers and draw them.
> Read an adventure in the Bible.
> Make someone happy.
> Study about a special creature and discover what lesson it teaches.

Holy: morally and spiritually excellent or perfect, and to be revered
Celebration: commemoration, observance, festival
Sabbath: day of rest
Eternity: infinite time

Words to Know

Your Choice

I understand that God made a special day each week so I could get to know Him better. I want to show that I love Him by remembering His special day. I want to learn more about God and His Sabbath gift.

Sign your name here: _____

CHAPTER 4

A Key For Eric

The Trinity And The Angels

The twins learned that God, the Holy Spirit, and Jesus worked as a team to create the world. This special team is called the Trinity because it has three members. They also discovered that God has many helpers called angels.

Like Eric and Susan, you have a special guardian angel that stays with you at all times.

If you look into a tide pool, you will see a creature that looks like a miniature palm tree. Every few seconds the great ocean waves send tons of water rushing into the pools where the sea palms live.

They crash, then swirl about, pulling on the tiny palms as they return to the sea. God gave these palms a special "holdfast" made up of many strong threads. This anchors them to the rocky walls of the pool. Otherwise they would be torn lose and tossed into the raging sea.

Your angel is like a "holdfast," protecting you and helping you hold onto your belief in God.

Some people have seen angels disguised as humans. Remember, even though angels are invisible, they are always with you, helping you hold fast to your rock, Jesus.

Dive Into The Bible

1. Write the names of the three members of the Trinity below._____

   _____ _____ 2 Corinthians 13:14

2. When Jesus lived on earth, He called God, Father. People could see Jesus and that

   made it possible for them to know what _____ is like. John 14:9

3. The Bible says that the _____ helped in the creation

   of the world. Genesis 1:2

4. The Holy Spirit also helped give me the _____ that tells me the

   _____ about God. 2 Peter 1:20 and 21

5. Helpers called angels, are _____ and _____.

   Psalm 103:20

Search For Buried Treasure

Group Discussion

Angels helped the apostle Phillip find a man who wanted to understand more about God. How can angels help me find others who need to hear about Him?
Read the story of Phillip in Acts 8:26.

An angel can appear when you least expect it. Read the verses below and write the names of the people that angels appeared to and helped.

Luke 2:8   _____

Luke 1:26   _____

Matthew 1:20   _____

Angel: attendant or messenger of God
Trinity: group of three
Guardian: defender, protector, or keeper
Messenger: person who carries a message

Words to Know

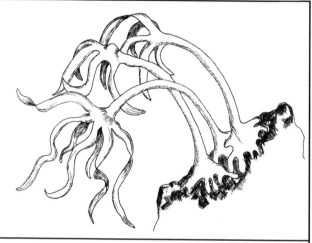

Sea Palm

Description: Brown algae that grows to 3' tall. Looks like a miniature palm tree with very flexible stems that bend with each crashing wave. Connects to rocks with holdfasts made of many strong fibers.

Habitat: Thrives in temperate waters of the Pacific coast of North America. Chooses wave-swept, rocky beaches. Actually avoids calm water.

Comments: the holdfast system connects Sea Palms to the rocks so securely that limpet shells may choose to attach to the palms instead of the cliffs. Sea Palms live in clusters resembling a little forest.

Your Choice

Dear God, thank you for angels. Thank you for sending them as messengers. Thank you for my own guardian angel. I believe that everyone in heaven works as a team. Show me what I can do to be part of your team.

Sign your name here: _____

The In-and-Out Laws

The Good Health Laws

What's so bad about snacks and junk food?" Eric said. He couldn't believe there was ever a time when people were all healthy. Then Aunt Sally told him about Adam and Eve and showed him the eight special health laws.

God wants His sea creatures to be healthy just like people. The Queen Conch, one of His best creations, is soft and could easily be destroyed by its enemies. But God gave it a special piece of flesh called the mantle. Tiny doorways in the mantle take in calcium from the sea and transform it into a strong,

protective shell.

Like the Queen Conch, you need to take into your body the kind of food that will protect your health. You can also choose what information you will take into your brain so that it will be strong. Your mouth, eyes, and ears are like doorways. Whatever comes through these doorways changes your life.

God wants you to be in charge of these doorways, so He gave you eight health laws called the In-and-Out Laws. Study them in chapter five of *Treasures by the Sea*, then make a list of them in the blanks below.

Dive Into The Bible

1. The eight wonderful laws that protect me are:

   1. _____   5. _____

   2. _____   6. _____

   3. _____   7. _____

   4. _____   8. _____

2. Read 3 John 2. God wants me to enjoy _____ _____.

3. Another reason I should take care of my body is that it is home for the

   _____ _____. 1 Corinthians 6:19 and 20

4. I am very special. I was created _____ God. Genesis 1:26

Search For Buried Treasure

Group Discussion

Why does God want me to have a strong body and mind?
Read: 1 Corinthians 6:19, John 2:21.

A healthy body includes a strong mind. On the lines below, write five good things you can think about.

- _____
- _____
- _____
- _____
- _____

Mollusk: marine invertebrate having a soft un-segmented body, a mantle, and hard shell
Happiness: feeling or showing pleasure or contentment
Health: state of being well in body or mind

Words to Know

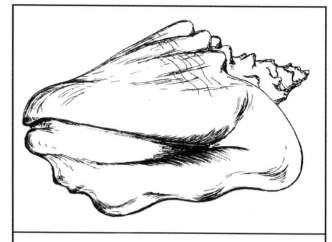

Queen Conch

Description: Large, rosy pink, thick conch shell that reaches over 12 inches.

Habitat: Likes shallow water. Cruises along the sand near eelgrass beds in the West Indies, Bermuda, and Florida.

Comments: When threatened or not feeding, the mollusk creature that makes the conch, shuts itself safety inside with a claw-like operculum or door. Often travels with a tiny conch fish that hides under a space created by the ruffled edge of the outer lip of the shell. Islanders slash the narrow, coiled end of the shell with a machete, making a large slit that causes the white meaty animal to slide out.

Your Choice

I know now that God made me special. He wants me to be happy and healthy. He gave me eight laws to help me choose how to live. I want to have a strong body and strong mind. God, please help me to follow your laws of health.

Sign your name here: _____

CHAPTER 6

Hooked

Satan And The Origin Of Sin

I can't believe you actually swallowed a fish hook," Eric said to the frightened sea gull. He sat in the sand guarding the bird while his sister and aunt ran to get help.

He also wondered why Adam and Eve had swallowed the lies of a snake. Eric knew that God warned them about an enemy who would be waiting at a certain tree in the garden. God told them they could avoid the enemy by staying away from the tree.

As long as they obeyed God, they enjoyed life in their beautiful garden home. But one day Eve wandered away from Adam's side. She spotted a snake entwined around a branch in the very tree God asked her to avoid. The snake spoke, inviting her to touch the fruit. It promised the fruit would make her smart like God. Foolishly, she believed the serpent's lies. She reached out, grabbed the fruit, then ate it.

Sea gulls will swallow almost anything. They often try to jam an entire sea star into their mouths. If it gets stuck, they will die. Adam and Eve, like foolish gulls, swallowed a lie that brought death to our world. You can read their story in the Bible. Find Genesis, Chapter 3.

Dive Into The Bible

1. God warned Adam and Eve not to disobey Him, or they would surely

   _____. Genesis 2:17

2. Who told the first lie? _____ Genesis 3:4

3. Who did Adam blame for his own disobedience? _____ Genesis 3:12

4. Eve said to God, "The serpent _____ me and I ate." Genesis 3:13

5. God told Adam and Eve the truth and they began to _____. Romans 6:23

6. When God came to visit Adam and Eve in the garden, they _____

   from Him. Genesis 3:8

7. How do you think God felt when He discovered Adam and Eve hiding from Him?

   _____

Search For Buried Treasure

Group Discussion

Why might I be afraid to admit I have done something wrong?
Read: Psalm 38:18, 1 John 1:9.

Nature Activity

Open your Nature Notebook. Make a list of creatures that use tricks to capture their prey.
Search for examples of these creatures. Visit a zoo or read a book.
Draw a picture of the creatures hiding. See if your friends can spot the creature.
Write a description of how each creature uses its tricks in the wild.
Example: The Flounder can change colors.

Obey: carry out a command; follow; observe
Trap: trick or betray a person into wrongful speech or act
Sin: breaking of divine or moral law, especially by a conscious act
Origin: a point at which something begins

Words to Know

Off the Hook

WARNING: Fish hooks and invisible fishing lines are harmful to seabirds, like gulls, looking for tasty treats. Bait used by fisherman often hides the dangerous hook.

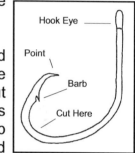

If a seabird gets hooked or entangled in a line, he cannot remove it without help. When no help is near, the line can wrap around the bird's legs and wings. A wound from the hook can become infected. Under these conditions, the innocent seabird will die.

How can you help a hooked bird?

The barb makes the hook difficult to remove. If the point and barb are protruding from the skin, a sharp wire cutter can be used to cut the point from the hook. Once the point and barb are removed, carefully push the hook back through the skin.

If you can't see the point and barb protruding from the skin, don't try to remove it yourself. Call a local wildlife care facility for help.

Your Choice

I believe that Satan tricked Eve at the Tree of the Knowledge of Good and Evil. I want to know and understand God's warnings. I want to listen to them and make good choices.

Sign your name here: _____

15

Villains And Heroes

Understanding Death

"What happens to dead people," Susan wondered. "Where are they?"

Did you ever wonder what happens to a person when they die? There are many different ideas about death and what happens to dead people. You can know the truth. Find out what God says about it in the Bible.

God created Adam and Eve to live forever. When they believed the lies of the serpent, Satan, death came into the their garden home.

Like Satan's lies, sea serpents are deadly. A single bite can kill an adult person. You are too smart to reach out and touch a sea serpent slithering past you in the ocean, but are you wise enough to recognize Satan's lies? Do you realize that choosing his ways brings death? The bad news is that when Adam and Eve disobeyed God, sin entered the world and everything God created began to die. The good news is that Jesus has overcome death and brought life.

God wants you to understand the truth about what happens to people when they die. You can get the answers straight from God. The Bible verses below will help answer your questions.

Dive Into The Bible

1. Who does the Bible tell us was the first person to die? _____. Genesis 4:8

2. After Abel died, what did he think about? _____ Ecclesiastes 9:5

3. Are the dead involved in activities that are happening in the world? The Bible says they have no _____ . Ecclesiastes 9:5 and 6

4. Lucifer brings death to our world. Jesus brings life. Jesus showed us His power over death when he brought his friend Lazarus back to life. He said that death is like a _____. John 11:11-14

5. Jesus made a promise to everyone who loves Him. He will raise the dead with a _____ _____. 1 Thessalonians 4:14-18

Search For Buried Treasure

Word Search
Find the words hidden below.

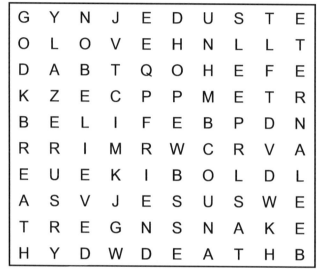

G	Y	N	J	E	D	U	S	T	E
O	L	O	V	E	H	N	L	L	T
D	A	B	T	Q	O	H	E	F	E
K	Z	E	C	P	P	M	E	T	R
B	E	L	I	F	E	B	P	D	N
R	R	I	M	R	W	C	R	V	A
E	U	E	K	I	B	O	L	D	L
A	S	V	J	E	S	U	S	W	E
T	R	E	G	N	S	N	A	K	E
H	Y	D	W	D	E	A	T	H	B

DEATH, JESUS, SNAKE, ETERNAL, DUST, LIFE, LAZARUS, FRIEND, LOVE, BOLD, BELIEVE, BREATH, GOD, SLEEP, HOPE.

Die: cease to live
Disobey: fail or refuse to obey; defy; rebel; ignore
Death: in John 11:11, Jesus refers to Lazarus' death as sleep
Sleep: naturally recurring condition of suspended consciousness

Words to Know

Description:
Sea snakes look like land snakes with flat bodies and paddle-like tails. The shape of their bodies helps them to slither through the water with ease. Nostrils on top of their heads enable them to breathe in oxygen while floating on the ocean surface. One breath can last for hours.

Habitat: Found in the Pacific Ocean, Indian Ocean, and the Caribbean Sea.

Comments: The venom of the South Pacific Beaked Snake is so deadly, one drop can kill five adult humans. A large group of sea snakes was once sighted traveling through the Strait of Malacca near Sumatra. It measured ten feet wide and sixty miles long. This type of gathering is called a snake slick.

Your Choice

I believe that Jesus has power over death. I know I can trust what His word says about dying. I will trust in Jesus to care for my life and the lives of those I love.

Sign your name here: _____

A Hero With Good News

The Plan Of Salvation

Exactly why did Jesus have to come here and die," Eric wondered. *"Couldn't He just kill Satan or something?"* At first, Eric didn't understand God's plan of salvation. But as he learned more, he felt amazed by the wonderful rescue plan.

In the beginning, God meant for Adam and Eve to live forever, enjoying their beautiful garden home. When they believed Satan's lies and rebelled against God's commands, they lost control of the world and Satan claimed it as his own territory.

God felt sad to lose the close friendship He enjoyed with Adam and Eve. It also hurt Him when Satan accused Him of not loving this world and the people He had created.

But God had prepared a plan to save what was lost. The amazing plan included the death of His Son, Jesus. It opened a way for you to understand the problem of sin and provided a solution.

Unlike a piece of useless driftwood, tossed about by the wind and waves, you can be sure of your future and feel confident that God loves you. This will become your strong belief as you read His messages to you in the following verses.

Dive Into The Bible

1. John 3:16 lets me know just how strong God's love is. God _____

    Jesus so I can _____ forever.

2. Salvation cost a lot. It cost Jesus His life. For me it is a _____

    _____. Ephesians 2:8

3. God loves me so much that He calls me His _____. 1 John 3:1

4. One reason sin is so terrible is that it brings _____. Romans 6:23

5. God invented a plan to solve the sin problem. In His plan, _____ would

    _____ to pay for my sins. Romans 5:8

6. It is not part of God's plan for me to save myself, or pay for my own sins. My part is

    to accept His plan and say, "I _____ in Jesus."

Search For Buried Treasure

Group Discussion

How can I be sure I am saved by Jesus?
Read: Romans 10:9.

Word Scramble

Complete the words below by filling in the missing letters.

S __ L V A T __ __ N

__ __ N F E S S

B E __ __ __ V E

L __ V __

W O __ L __

O N __ Y S __ N

E T E __ N __ L

L __ __ E

> **Lost:** be deprived of, or cease to have, especially by negligence
> **Accuse:** charge with a fault or crime
> **Confess:** acknowledge or admit

Words to Know

Nothing can seperate us from God's love.
Not...

• _____

• _____

• _____

• _____

• _____

• _____

• _____

Romans 8:38, 39

Nature Activity

Take a walk along the beach, a lake, or river and look for driftwood cast upon the shore. A piece of driftwood can travel many miles, battered by rocks, sand, and waves. Finally it rests on the shore just waiting for you to come along. Why not start a driftwood collection?

Driftwood is interesting, but, unlike freshly cut and seasoned wood, you can't make anything useful from it.

Your Choice

I believe that God made the best plan to solve the sin problem. He sent Jesus to live and die for me. I confess that Jesus is the Son of God. I believe that God raised Jesus from the dead. Thank you God, for your Plan of Salvation.

Sign your name here: _____

Eric's Brittle Star

Faith In Jesus

Eric told Susan that he didn't see how he could ever be a good Christian. She knew that he worried a lot and found it hard to believe that God loved him. She began looking for a sea creature that could help him understand God's love.

One day they discovered a tiny, twitching brittle star beneath the rocks. Eric learned a lot from the brittle star.

If you lift a rock and spot a brittle star, it will dash for the next nearest rock. This is because a voice inside, called instinct, tells it that a rock is the best place to hide.

You are more wonderful than a brittle star and God gave you an even stronger instinct called faith. At birth He placed a spark of faith inside your heart to help you believe that He loves you. The more you choose to believe, the stronger your faith grows.

No matter how many times a rock is lifted from a bunch of brittle stars, they will hang onto their belief that a rock is the best place to hide. They will dash off toward another rock. No matter what dangers you face, you can choose to trust God when He says, "I am the Rock of your Salvation. Stay with Me."

Dive Into The Bible

1. What did Eric read in Ephesians 1:5 and 6 that gave him hope? Jesus

   _____ us and _____ us.

2. I can discover more good news written in Ephesians 1:7. Jesus

   _____ me and _____ me.

3. When I am right with God, I have _____. Romans 5:1

4. Because of all this good news, my faith in Jesus grows. I can choose to

   _____. Isaiah 26:4

5. Like Eric, I can ask God to give me _____. Luke 17:5

Search For Buried Treasure

Group Discussion

What will help my faith grow stronger?
Read: Romans 10:17, Luke 11:28,
Luke 8:21.

Nature Activity

Visit a nature center. Take your Nature Notebook with you. List five creatures that live by instinct.
Search for ways God's creatures obey the voice of instinct to help them to survive.
Draw a picture of each creature using one of its instincts.
Write an explanation of how each creature uses its instincts in the wild.
Example: hiding, escaping, hunting.

Faith: complete trust or confidence
Forgive: cease to feel angry or resentful toward; pardon; clear; acquit
Worship: homage or reverence paid to a deity; adoration or devotion
Measure: size or quantity found by measuring

Words to Know

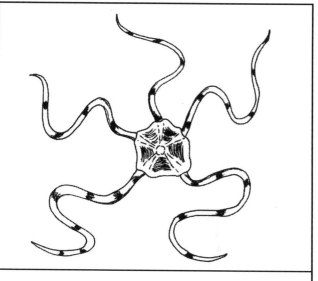

Brittle Star

Description: Member of the echinoderm family. Central disk may be round, pentagonal or scalloped. Smooth or hairy arms protrude from the disk.

Habitat: Under rocks in tide pools near low-tide line. Found from the Arctic to the Caribbean.

Comments: These secretive creatures hide beneath rocks during the day with limbs intertwined. They come out after dark to crawl about on top of rocks. Known to drop their limbs when touched.

Your Choice

Jesus, I believe that you are the Son of God. I believe that you love me. Make my faith grow strong. Help me to learn lessons from nature.

Sign your name here: _____

CHAPTER 10 The Decision

How To Accept Jesus' Gift

Dive into it!" Kevin shouted as the wave raged straight for Eric. "Like this." Suddenly Kevin disappeared into the rising wall of water.

Eric trusted Kevin and obeyed his instructions. He found, to his surprise, that the water beneath the wild, foaming wave was calm.

Is there sin or trouble in your life? Does it seem like a thundering wave is about to crash over you? Are you standing there like Eric, afraid, not knowing what to do?

Choose Jesus. He is a friend with experience facing waves of trouble. He knows how you feel. His love will be a calm, quiet place for you to dive into.

Satan has tried to destroy you, just as fishermen have tried to cut up sea stars and toss them into the sea. But, just as God gave the sea star the ability to heal and regenerate, He gives you a new life and heals your wounds.

Be smart like Eric. Believe, obey, and trust Jesus. Accept His free gift of forgiveness and dive deep into the ocean of His love. Now you belong to the One who is a faithful Friend. Now you live in certainty and peace.

Dive Into The Bible

1. I do have a choice. I can be a _____ to sin and die, or I can obey God and_____ Romans 6:16

2. When I am sick, I need a doctor. When I see my sins, I feel the need for
   _____. Mark 2:17

3. God wants me to live a life full of joy. He wants me to choose Him and repent, so that I will not _____. Luke 13:3

4. Read 2 Corinthians 7:10. To repent simply means I am _____ for sin and have a desire to stop sinning and become like Jesus.

5. Acts 5:31 gives me good news. God _____ repentance and forgiveness as free gifts. All I do is ask and I receive.

Search For Buried Treasure

Group Discussion

Group Discussion

Why did God make salvation a free gift?
Read: John 3:16, Ephesians 2:4-10.

The Great Sea Star Escape Maze

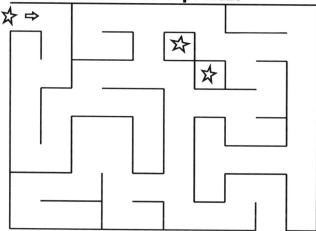

Repent: feel deep sorrow about one's actions
Christian: a person who believes in or follows the religion based on the teachings of Jesus Christ
Exercise: mental or spiritual activity, especially to develop a skill

Words to Know

M iracle of the Sea Star

Many years ago fisherman tried to destroy the sea stars that were eating the mussels and clams. The men collected thousands of sea stars, chopped them in half and tossed them back into the sea.

When this didn't work, they called some

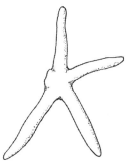

scientists for help. They discovered sea stars could not be destroyed by cutting them up. God made them able to regenerate from small pieces and grow new rays to replace the ones cut off.

Sea stars live in the **tide pool zone**. Some are so small they fit on your thumb. Others grow to be over twelve inches wide.

Stars are mostly brown, but may be red, yellow, or green. Some live on dangerous, wave-crashed rocks, others like the quiet protection of deep tide pools.

Your Choice

Jesus, I accept you as my Savior from sin. Thank you for making a way for me to escape the waves of sin. Thank you for dying for me.

Sign your name here: _____

CHAPTER 11 The Ugly Shell

Understanding Forgiveness

Why don't we just forgive that man?" Eric asked his father. Eric knew that not forgiving can be as dangerous as meeting a moon snail.

This snail cruises the sea bottom looking for a victim. When it finds one, it slithers onto the shell, spits out a drop of chemical that weakens it. Next it begins to scrape the softened shell with a set of sharp knife blades called a Radula. When a hole appears, the moon snail sticks a tube into the hole and sucks out the very life of the mollusk inside.

Have you been a victim? Has someone hurt you in some way? Do you feel angry and wish they would get what they deserve? This is a normal way to feel, but Jesus asks you to give these feelings to Him. He asks you to forgive. He wants you to let go of hate because it will weaken your faith. It will cut into your heart and destroy your life.

Forgiving doesn't mean that the hurt you experienced is no big deal. Sin hurts. Sin put God's Son on a cross. Forgiving doesn't mean that you ignore what happened. You might even need to tell someone about your problem.

Forgiving means that you choose to let go of your feelings of hurt and anger, so they will not grow into hate. You let Jesus give you His joy and peace instead. He will take care of punishing the other person. You will feel free.

Dive Into The Bible

1. Who is God willing to forgive? _____. Read Psalm 86:5.

2. Not only does God forgive me, He_____ my sins. Jeremiah 31:34

3. The prophet Isaiah paints a picture of what God does with my sins. He will

   _____ them out like a _____. Isaiah 44:22

4. I want God to forgive me, so I need to _____ others.

   Matthew 6:12,14 and 15

5. Jesus loved everyone. He even _____ the ones who nailed Him to

   the cross. Luke 23:34

Search For Buried Treasure

Group Discussion

Why is it important for me to forgive others?
Read: 1 John 1:9, Luke 17:4, Mark 11:26.

Escape the Giant Moon Snail

← Safe at Last

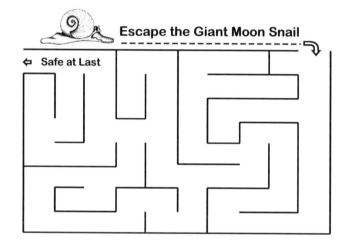

Predator: an animal naturally preying upon others
Forgive: cease to feel angry or resentful toward
Radula: a flexible tongue-like organ having rows of horny teeth on the surface

Words to Know

Giant Moon Snail

Description: Grows to more that 5" in diameter. Glides along just beneath the surface of the sand by beating millions of cilia on its broad foot. It leaves a wide trail behind it.

Habitat: Chooses muddy sand flats along the California coast that are exposed at low tide.

Comments: The moon snail is a cannibal, often killing other moon snails for food. It slithers over the mud, or even beneath it, searching for other sea shells. When it discovers a victim, it drills a hole in the shell by scraping repeatedly with a set of knife blades called a radula. Then the moon snail sucks the animal's flesh with a long snout called the proboscis.

Your Choice

Thank you, God, for forgiving my sins. I accept your gift of forgiveness. I want to forgive those who have hurt me. Please help me to forgive others, just like You forgive me.

Sign your name here: _____

CHAPTER 12
Strong Weaklings

How To Have Victory In Your Life

When Eric decided to choose Jesus, the desire to obey Him grew stronger. Eric also wanted to forgive others. He didn't want to carry hatred in his heart. He tried hard, but often failed. This made him feel cranky. The harder he tried, the more mistakes he made.

When you experience this, remember how Eric discovered that although the sand dollar looks weak, it's really strong. The sand dollar knows how to build inner strength. It creates pillars inside itself between its floor and ceiling. These tiny pillars make the sand dollar strong.

The God who created the sand dollar, and knows what it needs is the same One who made you. He knows your needs, too. He understands that obedience to His laws makes you happy, but that you can't obey without the miracle of an inner strength. He wants to be that strength for you.

Shout for joy! Jesus also gives you a "new heart" that loves to obey Him and hates sin. He gives you Himself. He lives within you providing you with inner strength. This is a miracle just like the inner pillars of the sand dollar.

Dive Into The Bible

1. When I choose Jesus as my Savior, He changes me. These verses tell me that _____ will do it! 1 Thessalonians 5:23,24

2. What really matters is _____. Ecclesiastes 12:13

3. Good news! God wants to give me a new _____ and _____ that desires to do what is right. Ezekiel 36:26 and 27

4. I can be strong in the Lord in His _____ + _____. Ephesians 6:10

5. 1 John 5:5 tells me that the ones who overcome sin are those who _____ that Jesus is the Lord.

6. 2 Chronicles 20:15 says that I cannot fight the battle against sin by trying. The battle belongs to _____.

Search For Buried Treasure

Group Discussion

How do I become strong inside like the sand dollar?
Read: 1 Corinthians 15:57, Hebrews 4:16.

Nature Activity

If possible, take your Nature Notebook and visit a beach at low tide.

Search for exposed sand bars. Run your fingers through the sand. Watch for a round, flat, brown, hairy, creature.

Draw a picture of a sand dollar in its hiding place.

Write a story about your discovery.

Victory: defeat of an enemy or opponent
Righteous: morally right; virtuous; law-abiding
Pillar: slender vertical structure used as a support
Miracle: extraordinary event; remarkable occurrence

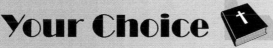

Words to Know

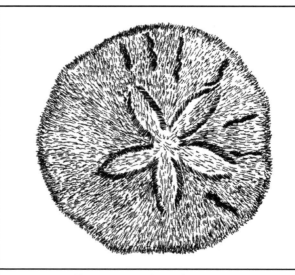

Eccentric Sand Dollar

Description: An echinoderm. 3" wide disc covered with short spines. A five-pointed star pattern on top side consists of tiny holes for breathing tubes.

Habitat: Groups of one hundred in sand along coastline or sheltered bays. Live at the low tide line up to 130' deep, from Alaska to Baja California.

Comments: Sand dollars lay flat when water is rough, but like to stand vertically in calm water. They filter feed, staying upright by partially burying themselves in sand. Juveniles swallow sand. It weights them enough to keep them on the sea floor.

Your Choice

I accept Jesus' gift of obedience. I accept His strength inside my heart. I choose to stay wrapped up in Jesus. I will stay close to Jesus through prayer.
I want to learn more about God by studying His Word and nature.

Sign your name here: _____

CHAPTER 13

Eyes for Susan

Understanding The Bible

It's wonderful that someone with sight can help a blind person "see." Susan helped Lisa by describing the beach and leading her to the edge of the water where she could feel it wash over her feet and taste the salty spray. She also sat on the wet sand and formed part of a sand castle. In this way, she experienced the truth of what a beach was like even though she could not actually see it.

Sin can hide God from view. This makes it difficult to understand what He is really like. Yet, God wants you to know Him. That is why He sent Jesus to this earth. Look at how Jesus treated people. Listen to what He said. When you know what Jesus is like, you know what God is like.

God gave you His Words in the Bible and a special helper, called the Holy Spirit, who helps you understand what you read.

The Holy Spirit knows God and He knows you. Like the wonderful Ghost Crab, He can see everything that is happening everywhere. He is with you to help you and to bring special gifts called "fruit." Discover more about the Holy Spirit in the verses below.

Dive Into The Bible

1. The Holy Spirit helps me _____. Luke 12:12

2. Romans 8:26 explains that the Holy Spirit is right with me to help me know

   _____.

3. He stood beside the prophets when they _____ the Bible. 2 Peter 1:21

4. He teaches me the _____ about God. John 16:13

5. Jesus promised that the Holy Spirit would always _____.
   John 14:16

6. Romans 8:11 tells me that the Holy Spirit_____ in me.

Search For Buried Treasure

Group Discussion:

Does everyone receive all the fruit of the Spirit?
Read: 1 Peter 4:10.

Fruit of the Holy Spirit

List the Fruit of the Holy Spirit below.
Read: Galatians 5:22,23.

1. _____   7. _____
2. _____   8. _____
3. _____   9. _____
4. _____
5. _____
6. _____

Gift: something transferred from one person to another without compensation
Invite: to request the presence of
Prophet: one who speaks divinely inspired revelations

Words to Know

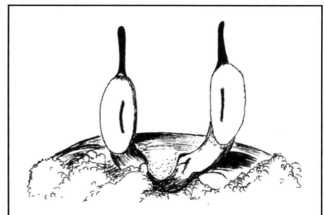

The Ghost Crab

Description: In the early morning, you might discover a Ghost Crab watching you with eyes that sit on the end of long stalks. These eyes can swivel around in a circle and each acts independently of the other. In this way the crab can be aware of its surroundings at all times, looking in different directions at once.
Habitat: They often cover themselves with sand, leaving only their eyes sticking out. They sit still, always watching everything from their hiding places.
Comments: The ability of these crabs to see everything around them, while not being seen themselves, helps you understand the invisible Holy Spirit who can know and see everything at once.

Your Choice

I understand that when I invite the Holy Spirit into my life, He brings wonderful benefits like joy, kindness, and self-control. I want to have this good fruit in my life. I invite the Holy Spirit to come into my life today and be my Helper.

Sign your name here: _____

CHAPTER 14 — Eric's Poriferan

Our Sinful Nature

You might swim right past a sponge and not recognize it. Sponges grow in odd shapes. They look like flower vases, basketballs, or clusters of tubes. The encrusting sponge is really different. It drapes itself over dead brain corals and rocks, like a blanket thrown over a bed.

Sponges are groups of cells. Each group performs a special job. Together the groups make up the living sponge.

If you grab a sponge with your bare hand you could get cut because there are tiny glass splinters, called spicules, inside. These form an inner skeleton that helps hold the sponge upright.

Sponge divers gather sponges and dump them into vats of chemicals that dissolve the spicules. After this treatment, dried sponges still feel rough unless you soak them in water before putting them to work.

Sponges teach you how Jesus works in your life. Like the sponge diver, He brings you up from the dark sea of sin. He washes you clean. He gives you a soft heart that loves Him. Day by day, He dissolves away the spicules of sin. Go ahead, get excited, because while He removes the spicules of sin, He covers you with His Robe of Righteousness. When God looks at you, He sees Jesus!

Dive Into The Bible

Three things happened when sin came into my world.

1. **First:** Sin brought physical _____. James 1:15

2. **Second:** I was born _____ to sin. I might not be interested in spiritual things because of this. I have a _____ nature. Romans 7:14

3. **Third:** I lost _____ _____. Romans 6:23

Three things that God did about the sin problem are:

1. God sent His Son to _____ for my _____. Romans 5:8

2. He gave me the gift of _____ _____ John 10:10

3. He made me His _____. John 15:15

Search For Buried Treasure

Nature Activity

In your Nature Notebook list five creatures that can be changed into something useful.
Search for these creatures around your home, school, or in a park.
Draw a picture of the creatures you discover.
Write a description of how these creatures can be changed.

Poriferan: a primitive multicellular marine animal
Spicule: small needle-like structure supporting the soft tissue of sponges
Endoskeleton: an internal supporting skeleton

Words to Know

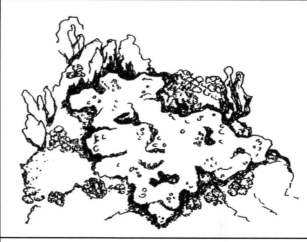

Velvety Red Encrusting Sponge

Description: A 1/4 inch thick mass that covers overhanging ledges and shaded crevices from low tide line to ten feet deep. Surface of the sponges are sprinkled with star-like breathing pores.

Habitat: Thrives in coastal waters from Washington to California.

Comments: Sponges are a community of cells, each performing a function for the good of the group. The sponge is home to the tiny Crimson Doris nudibranch that lays its eggs on the soft surface of the sponge. The nudibranch absorbs pigments as it eats the sponge, turning the eggs red. Lost cells are replaced in the sponge by the process of regeneration.

Your Choice

I am happy that Jesus wants to remove sin from my heart. I believe God sees Jesus when he looks at me. Thank you Jesus for finding me and taking me from the deep dark sea of sin.

Sign your name here: _____

CHAPTER 15

The Surprise

Baptism

Eric and Susan watched as a man plunged a young boy beneath an ocean wave. When he burst from the water he smiled at his friends who had gathered nearby. The sounds of laughter and singing swirled up the cliffs and into the sky. Eric and Susan learned that the boy had made the decision to follow Jesus and his baptism demonstrated that choice to his friends.

Have you made the decision to follow Jesus? Satan wants you to follow him. But he only offers temporary pleasure that ends in pain and death.

Look at Jesus. He offers life. Choose Him. Let Jesus wash away your sins. He wants to give you obedience, joy, and love as free gifts and promises to help you in every trouble you face. Come just as you are. He will accept you. He will give you a purpose for living. Be set free from guilt and receive eternal life.

Make your decision. Then show everyone that you have made the choice by being baptized. When you are baptized and the waters wash over you, remember, you are dying to sin, being cleansed, and rising to a new life with Jesus.

Dive Into The Bible

1. Once I believe Jesus' words and choose Him, I take an important step. This step is called _____. Mark 16:16

2. Jesus showed me how to follow Him by example. He was_____ in the Jordan River. Mark 1:9

3. I am so glad Jesus makes being saved so easy. My part is to _____, and be _____. Then, I will receive the _____ _____. Acts 2:38

4. What a wonderful Savior I have! When I'm plunged under the water at my baptism, I will rise to a new _____. Romans 6:4

Search For Buried Treasure

Group Discussion

At baptism you become part of God's family. Why is this important?
Read: Ephesians 4:15-16, Ephesians 5:26.

Nature Activity

In your Nature Notebook make a list of five creatures that depend on water to survive. **Search** around your home, school, or a park for creatures living in and depending upon water.
Draw a picture of the creature.
Write down the condition of the water. Is it clean, frozen, warm, quiet, protected?
Example: a pond with frogs, The sea with fish, or seals on ice.

Trench: a long, steep-sided valley in the ocean floor
Baptize: to dip beneath the water; to cleanse or purify
Water: A clear, colorless, odorless, and tasteless liquid, H_2O

Words to Know

Water Facts

Three percent of the water on Earth is freshwater. Seventy percent of the Earth is covered with water.

Human beings are sixty-six percent water. The human brain is seventy-five percent water.

Over 90% of the world's supply of fresh water is located in Antarctica.

3,400 cubic miles of water are locked within the bodies of living things.

The overall amount of water on our planet has remained the same thousands of years.

Most of the world's people must walk at least 3 hours to get fresh water.

Eighty percent of the fresh water used in the US is for irrigating crops and generating thermoelectric-power.

The deepest spot on Earth, Challenger Deep, is 35,802 feet (11,034 m) deep.

The highest tides on Earth are found in the Bay of Fundy east of New Brunswick, Canada. The tides can reach 53.5 feet.

The longest mountain range on Earth is the Mid-Ocean Ridge. It extends from the Arctic Ocean, through the Atlantic, and into the Pacific Ocean.

Your Choice

I know now that Jesus chose me. I want to choose Jesus. I want to follow His example and be baptized. I accept His offer to wash me clean from every sin. I know Jesus loves me and I choose to follow Him today.

Sign your name here: _____

CHAPTER 16

The Broken Law

The Ten Commandments

Have you ever wondered why there are so many laws? A smart SCUBA diver must learn and obey the dive laws. Some help him get to the ocean floor and others to return safely to the surface.

One of the most important diving laws states that a diver must NEVER HOLD HIS BREATH WHILE ASCENDING. When a diver begins to ascend to the boat, the dive law reminds him to move slowly and breathe out continually.

This law is important because as a diver ascends each air bubble inside his lungs gets bigger and bigger. If a diver holds his breath, the expanding air bubbles get trapped in his lungs. Eventually, if he does not burp out the excess air, his lungs will burst like an over-filled balloon.

God governs His universe with laws. These important laws protect your life, so He wants you to know and understand them. He also promises to give you power to obey them. Don't be afraid if you break a law. Ask God to forgive you. The verses below will help you discover God's laws. Read them, then ask yourself, "Why are laws important?"

Dive Into The Bible

1. God's commandments are _____, _____, and

   _____. Romans 7:12

2. The law helps me in that it gives me knowledge of _____.

   Romans 3:20

3. Romans 8:15 says that when I choose Jesus, He _____ me. I can now

   call Him _____.

4. Now I will want to obey Him, not to be saved, but because I _____

   Him. John 14:15

5. In Psalm 119:77 David calls God's law a _____.

Search For Buried Treasure

Group Discussion

Why do you think laws are important?
Read: Psalm 19:7, Psalm 119:18.

List God's special protection laws. You can find them in Exodus 20.

1. _____
2. _____
3. _____
4. _____
5. _____
6. _____
7. _____
8. _____
9. _____
10. _____

The Diver's Law:

A wise diver knows that the secret of surviving the dangers of the deep is to obey the laws created to protect his life.

1. Protect the reef. Learn and practice good buoyancy skills.
2. Breathe continuously and never, never hold your breath while scuba diving.
3. Keep gear in good condition. Service regularly.
4. Always dive with a buddy.
5. Wear proper protection in cold water and avoid overheating.
6. Pace yourself to avoid overexertion.
7. Practice proper weighting. Wear the right amount of weight.
8. Carry an alternate air source.
9. Plan your dive. Dive your plan.
10. Stay within dive table limits.

Your Choice

I am glad God made laws. I know they will help me be safe and healthy. I know God's laws will protect me. Thank you, Jesus, for showing me your laws. I choose to follow your laws.

Sign your name here: _____

CHAPTER 17 Pagurus

Prophecy And The Prophets

Eric wondered if God is like Pagurus the hermit crab. He crawls inside his shell, slams a red claw over the opening, and refuses to come out. Eric struggled to get to know a God he couldn't see.

God isn't hiding, but He knows that you might feel the way Eric did. He wants you to know Him and become His close friend. This is why He invented prayer, a type of heavenly E-mail system. Prayer helps you and God stay connected and feel closer.

He also created the fantastic sea creatures to help you understand what He is like. Each creature gives you a different picture of God, helping you know Him.

God sends special messengers, called prophets. He gives them important information and instructs them to write everything down so you know what He is trying to say to you.

Ellen White was one of these messengers. Reading her messages helps you know what to do in times of trouble and how to avoid making mistakes. Like all prophets, her messages encourage you as you walk with God. They help you communicate with Him.

Dive Into The Bible

1. God communicates to me through prophets. Both men and_____ could be prophets. Philip's daughters had the gift of _____ . Acts 21:8 and 9

2. Amos 3:7 says that God is eager to reveal His _____ to His servants the _____. I can learn about the future by reading their messages.

3. Jeremiah 28:9 says that a true prophet's words will come _____.

4. One way I can tell if a prophet is speaking from God is to see if his words agree with the _____ and the _____. Isaiah 8:20

5. God does not hide Himself from me like the hermit crab. He wants to communicate with me. He is not trying to keep truth a _____. Isaiah 45:19

Search For Buried Treasure

Group Discussion

How can I know the difference between a false and true prophet?
Read: Matthew 7:16,20.

God's Prophets

List four reasons God inspires prophets. 2 Timothy 3:16

_____

_____

_____

_____

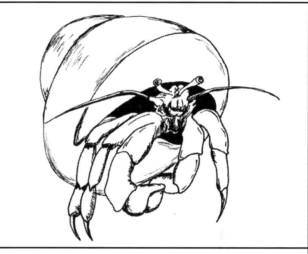

Pagurus (Hermit Crab)

Description: A Crustacean less than one inch long. Thin, hairy legs. Pinchers have white or blue speckles.

Habitat: Alaska to Baja California. Scampers among kelp holdfasts from near shore tide pools down as deep as 50 feet.

Comments: Favors Black Turban Snail shells. Locates empty shell, checks it for size by turning it in its claws. Drops old shell and quickly inserts itself into new shell. Some Pagurus catch the scent of dead snails and head for the location. They compete for the shell with other hermits. Finally a crab decides the new shell is a perfect fit and moves in.

Crustacean: aquatic creatures with hard exoskeleton
Communicate: to convey knowledge or information
Prophet: a person who speaks by divine inspiration
Inspire: to affect, guide, or arouse by divine influence

Words to Know

Your Choice

I know that you want to communicate with me, God. Thank you for sending prophets to write down your messages. I want to understand your messages. I choose to read them carefully. Help me to understand.

Sign your name here: _____

Taught by a Fish

The 2300 Day Prophecy

"Come quick!" Eric shouted. "There are thousands of fish all over the place."

Grunion fish swirl onto California beaches with the highest Spring tides. These silvery fish lay thousands of eggs that will be safe from the waves that follow. Weeks later, when the eggs are ready to hatch and the tides are again high and flood the beach, the eggs will wash into the sea. A new generation of grunion will live because of the perfect timing of God. You can count on this miracle recurring every year.

Have you ever wanted to count on someone, but they kept breaking their word. Perhaps they promised to play ball with you on Tuesday, but never showed up. Then they set a time to take you to town on Thursday, but didn't come. You soon learned not to count on them. They couldn't be trusted.

God wants you to count on Him. He keeps His word. He tells you, through His prophets, what will happen in the future. When you read the Bible prophecies, you can see past events and realize that God keeps his promises. The 2,300 year prophecy described in Daniel 8 and 9 is one of these important prophecies.

Dive Into The Bible

1. Write the dates into the five pillars of the great 2300-year prophecy.

   1   **2**   **3**   **T**   **4**   **5**

   _____ B.C.   _____ B.C.   _____ A.D.   _____ A.D.   _____ A.D.
   You can find these dates in Chapter 18, on page 120, in *Treasures by the Sea*, by Sally Streib.

2. Read Daniel 9:25. What event marks the beginning of this prophecy?

   _____.

3. What happens at the end of this prophecy in 1844? _____.

4. Revelation 1:3 says that if I listen to God's prophets and obey their words, I will be

   _____.

5. God sent prophets so I could have _____. Romans 15:4

Search For Buried Treasure

Nature Activity

Walk around your home, school, or in a park. Take your Nature Notebook.

Search for signs that tell you creatures may be nearby.

Draw pictures of the signs you find.

Write down an explanation of each sign.

Example: animal tracks: Who was here?
Flower buds: When will the plant flower?

Prophecy: a divine utterance of a prophet that comes true

Prophetic Time: one day in prophecy equals one year

Sign: something that suggests the presence or existence of a fact, condition, or quality

Words to Know

California Grunion

Description: Thin, silver fish that grow up to six inches in length.

Habitat: Lives beyond the surf zone. Found from San Francisco to Baja California.

Comments: On second, third, and fourth nights after a full moon in March, April, May and June, grunions leap high onto the beaches in southern California. The female digs a hole with her tail, deposits the eggs and catches the next wave back to the sea. A male grunion fertilizes the eggs and follows her back to the sea. The eggs will remain beyond the reach of the waves for ten days. The eggs hatch at the moment the next highest tide occurs and are washed into the sea. The timing is perfect.

Your Choice

Thank you, Jesus, for giving me signs. I believe you want me to know that you are coming back soon. Now I know I don't have to be afraid. I choose to watch for you to come and to trust your signs.

Sign your name here: _____

Escape!

Running From Temptation

ou make hundreds of decisions every day. You smell something tantalizing and choose to eat it or leave it alone. You hear music and must decide to change the channel or go on listening. Thoughts come into your head and you must put them aside or dwell on them. Advertisements in magazines, TV, books, videos, the Internet, appeal to your desires and demand your attention.

Satan is better at entrapment than the Giant Green Anemone. He waves temptations in front of you, just like the anemone waves the flower-like petals that make it look so innocent. Just as the anemone is a dangerous enemy to some sea creatures, Satan and his enticing suggestions are dangerous to you.

On the other hand, God offers you real excitement and joy. He invites you to climb a mountain, help someone in need, learn a new skill, explore a coral reef, play an instrument, or read a great book.

Kevin taught Eric to ask three questions before making a choice. Will this make me want to know God better? Can I ask God to join me in this activity? Will this choice bring lasting joy to me and others?

Dive Into The Bible

1. Temptation comes to _____. 1 Corinthians 10:13

2. Being tempted is not a sin. I must not _____. Proverbs 1:10

3. Read 2 Peter 2:9. God is a friend who knows how to _____ me.

4. Philippians 4:8 tells me to think certain things. Some of them are:_____

   _____

   _____

5. 1 John 2:1 says that Jesus can keep me from falling into Satan's traps. But, if I

   make a mistake, Jesus will _____.

Search For Buried Treasure

Nature Activity

In your Nature Notebook make a list of animals that use traps to catch their prey. **Search** around your home or school for these hidden traps.
Draw a picture of the traps that you find.
Write down an imaginary warning to the creatures that might get trapped.
Example: Spider with a web.

Entrapment: to lure into danger, difficulty, or a compromising situation
Lure: something that tempts or attracts with the promise of pleasure or reward
Temptation: something tempting or enticing
Deliver: to set free, as from misery, peril, or evil

Words to Know

Giant Green Anemone

Description: Looks like a flower with waving blue-green tentacles. Grows up to twelve inches high and ten inches wide. Grabs prey with sticky tentacles, pushes it into a mouth, spitting out bones and shell.

Habitat: Lives in tide pools near shore. Can live up to fifty feet deep. Survives on wave-tossed coastlines from Alaska to Panama.

Comments: Although it is a loner, it may live close enough to touch the tentacle tips of another anemone. Senses presence of food by chemical changes in the water. Immediately expands its body, waving the circle of tentacles about. Tentacles reach out and entrap food particles, moving them to the mouth.

Your Choice

I'm glad Jesus has made a way for me to escape the traps of sin. I want to accept His help. I choose to think about good things, and to watch for the sneaky traps of the Devil. I want God to be with me always.

Sign your name here: _____

CHAPTER

20

The Law of Life

Receiving And Giving

D r. Foster took his Sabbath School class to the beach. They formed a circle around a large tide pool. He asked them to observe creatures crawling over the sand, swishing through the water, clinging to the rocks, and peaking from beneath kelp fronds. The kids soon discovered that every creature lives by the law of receiving, then giving to others.

God also lives by this law. He calls it the Law of Life. He asks you to live by it because it is the best way for everyone to be happy. He gave you His love and He wants to receive love from you in return.

The problems started when Satan decided that he didn't want to live by the Law of Life. He thought he could invent a better way—take what you can get for yourself and look out for number one.

As part of the Law of Life, God asks you to share ten percent of your income with Him. He calls it a tithe. He also asks for the seventh day of every week. This time is called Sabbath. Giving your time and money to God and His cause brings great blessings to you as well as a happiness that lasts. What you give, God promises to return to you with increase.

Dive Into The Bible

1. Jesus asks me to give as God _____. Deuteronomy 16:17

2. God loves for me to give with a _____ heart. 2 Corinthians 9:7

3. I am a partner with Jesus when I bring _____ into His storehouse. Malachi 3:10

4. God gives me the _____ to work and earn money. Deuteronomy 8:18

5. Remember! The Law of Life is to _____, then _____.

6. God wants to bless me. He asks me to do as Abraham did when he gave a _____ of everything. Genesis 14:20

Search For Buried Treasure

Tide Pool Life

Life in a tide pool is fantastic and bizarre. Creatures and plants of every size, shape, color, and habit, live beneath rocks, under the sand, and in tiny crevices between boulders. Each one receives life from its surroundings and gives back to promote life in the pool. No creature exists without the help of other animals and plants in the pool. This is how God wants you to live with your family and friends.

Group Discussion:

What do I have that I can give to God? How is it possible to have more by giving tithe and offerings to God?
Read: John 6:38.

Can you identify the creatures in the tide pool? Write the number from the list below that matches the tide pool creature in the picture. On a separate piece of paper create your own tide pool. Use the pictures in your workbook for help.

1 Blue Mussels
2 Black Abalone
3 Giant Green Anemone
4 Brittle Star
5 Chestnut Cowrie
6 Pagurus in Black Turban
7 Sea Palms

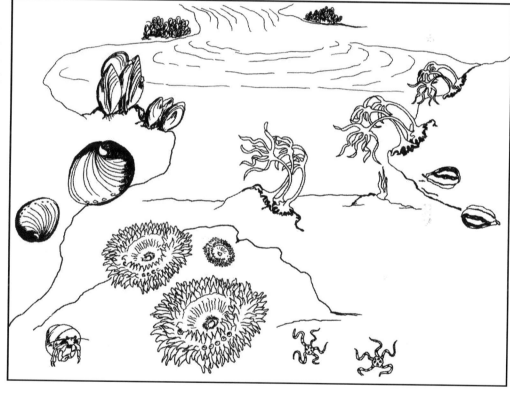

Your Choice

I want to live like the creatures of the tide pool. I want to give to my family and friends, and not just take. I believe that the Creator wants me to share the good things He has given me with the people around me.

Sign your name here: _____

43

Valuable Gifts

Spiritual Gifts

When Eric and Susan chose to follow Jesus, they discovered good news. They learned that God gave them special abilities called Spiritual Gifts. This idea made them feel valuable.

As they watched the creatures in the tide pools it became clear that variety made the pools exciting and interesting. They noticed that every fish had a different shaped tail to help it survive in its special place. This knowledge helped them see that God also has a special plan for every person.

They learned that even though they were like a grain of sand among millions of people, they were not small or insignificant. They discovered that just as a scientist can make fantastic things from something as common as sand, God could create a miracle in their life.

Talents are present within you at birth, but Spiritual Gifts are given to you at your re-birth when you accept Jesus. Often these are similar and part of your talents, but you will use your Spiritual Gifts to build up the family of God. Talk with your friends, teachers, and family. Talk with God. Explore the verses below and discover more about Spiritual Gifts.

Dive Into The Bible

1. God does not want me to be ignorant concerning my _____

   _____. 1 Corinthians 12:1

2. I may receive a different gift than my friends have, but the same _____

   gives the gift. 1 Corinthians 12:4 and 12

3. God wants me to use my special gift to _____ others. 1 Peter 4:10

4. Some of the gifts are:_____ _____ _____

   _____ _____ _____1 Corinthians 12:7-11 and 28.

   Choose one and describe what you think that gift could be used for.

6. Just as fish have different tails for special needs, I am _____.

Search For Buried Treasure

Fish tails come in many varieties. Each tail is designed by God to help that fish find its own place in the sea. Each design is for a special purpose. God also created people to be different and gives them a special purpose in life.

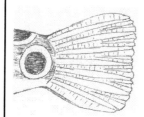

Rounded Tail
The rounded tail helps the Figure-Eight Puffer push through the water. It also keeps it upright as it steers between rocks and corals.

Deeply forked Tail
The Dolphin Fish cannot accelerate quickly, but it can build up great speed and cruise for long periods of time.

Fan-Shaped Tail
A fan-shaped tail provides sudden acceleration to the Great Barracuda. It waits motionless for a passing prey, then darts after it like a silver bullet.

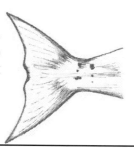

Triangular Tail
The triangular shape of his tail allows a strong swimmer like the Sockeye Salmon, to maneuver well and maintain long open-water swims in the sea.

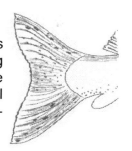

Gifts are **FREE from the Holy Spirit** . Read 1 Corinthians 12:8-11 and Ephesians 4:11 and list some of them below

1. _____
2. _____
3. _____
4. _____

On a separate piece of paper complete the following sentences. They will help you to discover more about the person you are becoming.

- The activities I enjoy most are...
- People say, "you are really good at..."
- I find it easy to...
- God seems to be moving me toward...
- Some people want me to...
- I think I could...

Your Choice

I believe that God made me unique. Thank you, God, for giving me special abilities. Help me learn how to use those special abilities. I choose to enjoy being myself, the way you made me, and not copy someone else.

Sign your name here: _____

The Intruder

Mark Of Obedience

When we keep the Sabbath, we show our loyalty to God," Eric thought. *"I want to be loyal to God."*

Though Eric made a decision to obey God, he felt fear growing inside him. It grew like the ice plants on Anacapa Island. Discouraging thoughts crept into his mind. He worried that his fears would push the good thoughts aside, like the enemy ice plants pushing out all the native plants that belonged on Anacapa Island.

You are learning new and exciting lessons from the Bible and nature. Have you had thoughts similar to Eric's? You love God and want to be loyal to Him. You know that the loyalty of those who live at the end of time will be tested. You have learned that Satan will try to force everyone to obey him instead of God.

God doesn't want you to worry. Remember, He understands every one of your fears. Because you chose Him and desire to obey Him, He gives you the special mark that sets you apart as His loyal friend. Have faith in His ability to uproot the ice plants of sin in your life. His power is strong enough to keep you loyal to Him in all circumstances.

Dive Into The Bible

1. Satan is at war against God and with me because I am loyal. I _____
   Him and _____. Revelation 12:17

2. Isaiah 14:14 tells me that Satan stopped being loyal to God. He wanted to be like
   _____. This does not mean to have His loving
   character, but to take over God's throne.

3. One sign that I am loyal to God is to obey the commandments in Exodus 20:8. I keep
   the _____ holy.

4. Read Exodus 20:9, 10 and 11. God made the _____ after He created
   the world in _____ days.

5. When I obey God, it shows that I _____ Him. John 2:3-5

Search For Buried Treasure

 Nature Activity

In your Nature Notebook make a list of five animals that rest.

Search around your home for some of these animals.

Draw a picture of the animals you find. Show what they look like when they are resting.

Write down the reasons why these animals need to rest.

Example: a pigeon roosting, dog napping, a cat sleeping in the sun.

Intrude: to enter by force; to invade
Loyalty: a feeling or attitude of devoted attachment and affection
Crystalline: resembling crystal, as in transparency or distinctness of structure or outline

Words to Know

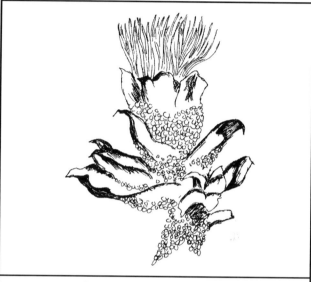

Crystalline Ice Plant

Description: Chunky, succulent, plant sprinkled with white blooms that look like small paint brushes. Absorbs moisture from the sea breeze. Water forms droplets on the plant's exterior that resemble crystals.

Habitat: Tolerates arid soil, drought and salty conditions.

Comments: A native of South Africa, this ice plant probably arrived on the wings of a visiting bird or drifting debris. It takes over, pushing other plants out.

Your Choice

I want to be loyal to God. I believe that God gave me His commandments to help me have a better life. I want to show my loyalty to Him by obeying all of His commandments.

Sign your name here: _____

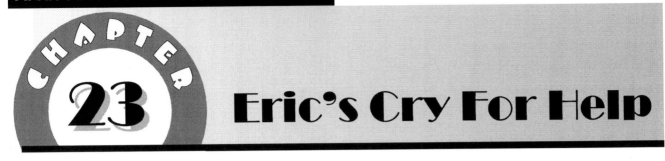

CHAPTER 23 Eric's Cry For Help

The Second Coming Of Christ

Eric and Susan learned that Jesus gave a list of signs that would help them know that the time of His second coming was near.

Aunt Sally pointed out the Golden Coreopsis flowers that burst into bloom on the tiny island of Anacapa, shouting the arrival of Spring. She explained that the flower's bold colors can be seen from the coast of California through binoculars and that this color is a sign that Spring will soon arrive.

Although God has not told you the exact date of Jesus' return, He does want you to know that the time is near. Just as the Golden Coreopsis on Anacapa announces the nearness of Spring, the signs described by Jesus in Matthew let you know that He will soon come. Because you believe He has saved you and is working in your life, the knowledge that Jesus will come soon should make you happy.

God is excited that He will see you and talk with you soon. Perhaps He walks through the empty streets of the New Jerusalem and into the home He has made for you. He imagines your laughter filling the golden rooms.

Dive Into The Bible

1. Jesus promised that He is going to _____. John 14:3

2. Jesus warned me that there will be trouble in the days before He returns. One problem will be the _____ leaders who refuse to teach the truth. Matthew 24:24

3. The first time Jesus came, He died on a cross. The second time He comes will be different. He will come with _____ and great _____. Matthew 24:30

4. When you hear Jesus sound His trumpet, the _____ will rise right up from their graves. 1 Thessalonians 4:15-17

Search For Buried Treasure

Group Discussion

How will the coming of Jesus be like lightning in the sky?
Read: Matthew 24:26.

Giant Coreopsis

Description: A yellow daisy-like flower growing in groups atop 2-4' stalks.

Habitat: Found on Anacapa island off the California coast.

Comments: This island plant, often called a tree sunflower, sits dormant most of the year. In early Spring it bursts into golden blooms that can be seen by observers on the California coast. The dark, stout, woody stalks growing in masses about the island give the appearance of miniature forests.

7 Reasons to be happy that Jesus is coming:

1. I belong to the family of God.
2. My sins are covered by His blood.
3. I'm covered by His righteousness.
4. He is changing me.
5. He knows the date when he will return.
6. He has given me signs to let me know the time is near.
7. He keeps His word. I trust Him.

Your Choice

I trust Jesus to make me ready for His return. I know He wants to be with me and I want to be with Him. I am looking forward to His soon return. Thank you, Jesus, for making a way for me to be with you in heaven.

Sign your name here: _____

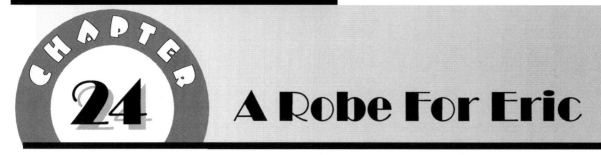

CHAPTER 24 A Robe For Eric

The White Robe Of Jesus

In Eric's dream he stood in God's courtroom and every mistake he ever made passed before him. He screamed in terror. When Eric awoke he learned that he didn't need to be afraid. He could receive a free gift, a special white covering called the Robe of Righteousness.

The cowrie shell is a beautiful example of how a covering can save. Chestnut Cowries live under rocky ledges along the California coast. The cowrie has a mantle, or cover, that wraps around its shell. The mantle covering not only creates and colors the shell, but it also hides the shell from its enemies. A predatory crab, dashing up to a cowrie, finds it almost impossible to grab and crush the shell. The claw just slips off the slimy mantle. What a fantastic covering!

You can choose to be wrapped in a special covering called the Robe of Righteousness. When God looks at you, He sees the goodness or righteousness of Jesus.

And when Satan reaches out with a claw of temptation, he can't get a hold on you. Jesus causes Satan's temptations to slip right off. You will shine with joy and be as beautiful as the Chestnut Cowrie.

Dive Into The Bible

1. I know that I have _____ and come short of God's glory. Romans 3:23

2. Nothing good that I can ever do will save me. My sins must be washed away by

   Jesus. His _____ washes away all my sins. 1 John 1:7

3. When I confess my sins, He is faithful to _____ and

   _____. 1 John 1:9

4. Righteousness, or being like Jesus, comes through believing in Jesus and receiving

   His _____. Romans 3:24

5. I can have joy because Jesus covers me with a _____ of

   _____. Isaiah 61:10 I know He loves me and accepts me.

Search For Buried Treasure

Group Discussion

Why are some people afraid of the coming judgment?
Read: Romans 2:16, 1 John 4:17-18.

How to Overcome Fear

I'm unafraid of the future and I'm unafraid of the judgment because I know _____ and I have _____.
Read 2 Timothy 1:12

Mantle: something that enfolds, envelopes, or covers
Righteousness: action in accord with divine or moral law, free from sin or guilt
Fear: a feeling of agitation and anxiety caused by the presence or imminence of danger

Words to Know

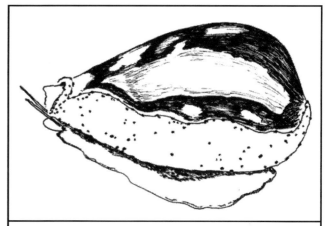

Chestnut Cowrie

Description: Oval, 2 5/8" by 1 3/8", chestnut brown shell edged in white or gray. Bottom is opened by a long, toothed slit. The mantle, like two slimy pieces of skin, comes out through this slit and wraps around the shell. It paints the pattern on the shell, makes it shine, and helps it resist enemies.

Habitat: Hides under ledges near sea weed and surf grass from Southern California to Baja.

Comments: The Chestnut Cowrie is difficult to find because of its camouflage mantle. It is a rare and valuable find for shell collectors. This amazing creature sits on its eggs like a bird in her nest.

Your Choice

I choose to accept the Robe of Righteousness that Jesus offers as a free gift.
I want to be wrapped in His protecting mantle.

Sign your name here: _____

CHAPTER 25 Threads Of Love

A Thousand Years With Jesus

Eric and Susan stood at the ocean's edge and stared at the clusters of Blue Mussel shells clinging to a rock. Wave after wave smashed against the small shells, but they held fast against the wave's powerful force. Strong byssus threads connected them securely to the rocks.

"That's just what I wanted to explain to you," Eric said. "God's love is strong. It's stronger than these byssus threads. He cares for us. He has plans for us. We have to hold onto Him."

While you may not spin byssus threads, you can hang on with threads of love. Every time you talk with Him, read the Bible or study His creation, you are connecting with God, like spinning a thread of love between your heart and His.

After Jesus returns to earth and takes you to heaven, you will live there for 1,000 years. Many wonderful things will happen during this time. You will have plenty of time to ask God questions. You will understand how God worked in your life during the time sin existed on earth. You will get to know Him even better than you do now. So cling to your Rock, Jesus! Spin those threads.

Dive Into The Bible

1. The wicked who die at the Second Coming and those who have died since the time of creation do not live again until the end of the _____ years. Revelation 20:5

2. People who loved Jesus and refused to worship Satan will _____ with Jesus for one thousand years after they are raised to life at the first resurrection. Revelation 20:4,6

3. Unable to tempt anyone for a thousand years, Satan goes right back to work to _____ people. But,_____ comes down from heaven. This is the end of _____. Revelation 20:7-9

4. After sin is destroyed by fire, God makes a new _____ and a new _____ . And God makes His _____ on earth. Revelation 21:1-3

Search For Buried Treasure

Group Discussion

Why does God to allow one thousand years to pass while I am in heaven and Satan is on earth with no one to tempt? Read: Revelation 20:2-4.

Nature Activity

In your Nature Notebook make a list of homes that creatures make.

Search for these homes in nature near your home, school, or at a park.

Draw a picture of the homes that you find.

Write down the location of the creature's home and when you found it.

Example: a robin's nest, a spider's web.

Bivalve: a shell with two valves or sides, held together by a strong muscle
Connect: to become joined, fastened, or linked together
Millennium: a thousand years

Words to Know

Blue Mussels

Description: Bi-valve or two sided shells, growing up to 4" long. Live in large groups called mussel beds that help individuals live safely as waves crash against them.

Habitat: Mussels cling to rocky surfaces with tough byssus threads. Thrive in frigid waters of Alaska and warm water as far south as Baja California.

Comments: These filter feeders sit, mouths slightly open, sipping sea water, removing oxygen and tiny food particles from the sea. A large mussel bed filters over 24 million metric tons of water a year. Mussels are able to detoxify themselves, getting rid of poisons in the water.

Your Choice

I believe that God has created a new home for me and all those that love Him and follow His commandments. I want to live with God for a thousand years in the heavenly home He has prepared for me.

Sign your name here: _____

CHAPTER 26

Unlocked At Last

The Brand New Earth

God's love was the only power strong enough to unlock Susan and Eric's hearts. His love healed their hurts. It washed away the guilt they felt because of their mistakes. It filled them with joy.

They learned that no matter what happened to them, they belonged to God. They chose to trust Him and look forward to going home with Him when He returned.

Do you want to belong to God's family? Have you discovered that His love is so strong it will last forever? Choose Jesus right now. Say, "I choose you, Jesus. I ask you to become my Friend and be with me forever. I ask you to forgive my sins and cover me with your Robe of Righteousness. I thank you for accepting me and forgiving me. Help me obey you and make the right decisions every day. Please come soon. I love you!"

Now realize that you can have confidence in your future. The same God who saves you, plans to give you a useful life right here in this world. He will give you joy as you live for Him. You can look forward to your life in heaven. You have made the right choice!

Dive Into The Bible

1. At the end of the thousand years, called the millennium, John saw the

   _____ _____ coming down out of heaven. Revelation 21:1,2

2. I want to see God create the new earth. The _____ will

   _____ there. 2 Peter 3:13

3. List several things you can expect to be missing on the new earth.

   _____,_____,

   _____, _____.

4. I can trust God to keep His promise. He will _____ again. Right

   now He is _____ a _____ for me. John 14:2,3

5. Wow! _____ will live on the new earth with me! Revelation 21:3

Search For Buried Treasure

Group Discussion

Why does God choose to live with humans on the New Earth instead of in Heaven? Read: John 14:2-3, Revelation 21:3.

You are a traveler to the New Earth. On the left notice some of the things you will leave behind. On the right, list opposite things that you will experience in the New Earth.

Old Earth	New Earth
1. Crying	1. _____
2. Fear	2. _____
3. Death	3. _____
4. Loneliness	4. _____
5. Hate	5. _____

Belong: to fit into a group naturally
Recreate: to impart fresh life to; refresh mentally or physically
Joy: intense and especially ecstatic or exultant happiness

Words to Know

Welcome to the New Earth!

The New Earth will be your forever home. Look up the texts below and discover what your new home will be like. Write the information you find on the blanks below.

Location: _____
2 Peter 3:13, Revelation 21:11

Name of Capital City: _____
Revelation 21:10

Light Source: _____
Revelation 21:23

Construction Materials: _____
Revelation 21:18-21

Water Supply: _____
Revelation 22:1

Food Supply: _____
Revelation 22:2

Inhabitants: _____
Matthew 5:5, Psalm 37:9, John 14:1-4

Your Choice

I believe that God has created a new home for me and all those that love Him and follow His commandments. I want to live with God in that heavenly home.

Sign your name here: _____

Also available by Sally Streib from Sea n' See Presentations.
www.seansee.net

Treasures by the Sea: $10.95 U.S. /$15.95 Can.
Quantity Ordered:_____
The story that started it all. Get set for adventure as Eric and Susan discover exciting truths about God's love.

27 Bible Truths for Kids Workbook: $10.00 U.S./$15.00 Can.
Quantity Ordered:_____
An adventure in discovering God through His Word and Nature. Now young people can learn the 27 main teachings of the Bible in a unique way that combines the story of Eric's and Susan's adventures in nature with lessons from the Bible.

27 Bible Truths for Kids Workbook, Teacher's Edition: $20.00 U.S./$30.00 Can.
Quantity Ordered:_____
Includes answers to questions and activities in the kids workbook. Also includes additional activities, object lessons, and instruction on how to use nature and the Bible to teach truth you young people.

Triton's Treasure, Book One, Choosing Jesus: $10.95 U.S./$15.95 Can.
Quantity Ordered: _____
Learn how to choose Jesus as your Savior. Author Sally Streib shares 14 real life adventures and spiritual lessons from her time in and around the sea.

Video—Scubaventures Volume I: $14.95 U.S./$22.50 Can.
Quantity Ordered: _____
As seen on Three Angels Broadcasting Network. Sally shares real life adventures and introduces new and exciting sea creatures that teach lessons about God's love. 30 min.

Video—Scubaventures Volume II:$14.95 U.S./$22.50 Can.
Quantity Ordered: _____
More exciting stories and adventures with Sally. 30 min.

God's Fantastic Sea Creatures: $9.95 U.S./$15.00 Can.
Quantity Ordered: _____
Nature Object Lessons to help you discover God's love in nature.

Discover God's Lessons in Nature: $9.95 U.S./$15.00 Can.
Quantity Ordered: _____
Discover how to find and understand Nature Object Lessons. Sally shares her easy to follow step-by-step approach to decoding the secrets of God's Creation.

The Abalone Message: Book and Abalone Shell Combo: $15.95. U.S./$24.00 Can.
Quantity Ordered: _____
Book/shell combo subject to availability.
Sally discovered over 70 exciting messages about the character of Christ. In this study guide she reveals her favorites and helps you discover messages the Creator wrote to you.

To order these and other books visit our web site at:
www.seansee.net or your local **Adventist Book Center.**

You may also order by sending check or money order to:
Sea n' See Presentations
1783 Forest Drive #221
Annapolis, MD 21401-4229

Shipping: Please add $4.00 for the first book/video and $2.00 for each additional book.
Please send my order to:

Name : _____

Address :_____

City :_____ State :_____ Zip Code : _____